# 2

## Teacher's Book

# Recorder Duets
## *from the* Beginning

## John Pitts

Chester Music Limited
(A division of Music Sales Limited)
8/9 Frith Street, London W1V 5TZ

Duet playing brings extra pleasure to all involved, and with it an incentive to learn new notes and rhythms in order to succeed. A simultaneous development of listening skills and concentration is also required for successful ensemble playing.

*Recorder Duets from the Beginning Books 1, 2* and *3* provide a wide range of repertoire to encourage duet playing by descant recorder players, both accompanied and unaccompanied. All the items are carefully graded, both in range of notes (pitches) included and in the level of difficulty. It is expected that players using Book 2 will have already reached the end of *Recorder from the Beginning Book 2*, in the author's widely popular teaching scheme.

Early pieces have matching rhythms in both parts, making it easier for the players to keep in time together. Then some independence of parts is gradually introduced, including the use of imitation and counting of rests, plus more sophisticated rhythms.

The Pupil's Books include guitar chord symbols, and the Latin American items have suggestions for use of percussion instruments. The Teacher's Books include piano accompaniments for all the duets as well as the Latin American percussion parts.

In keeping with the 'repertoire' nature of the books, only a minimum of teaching help or explanation is given. Where more help is required it is best to refer to the appropriate pages of the teaching scheme *Recorder from the Beginning*.

# Contents

# Spring (from The Four Seasons)  Vivaldi

# Ade, zur guten Nacht    German

# Gay Gordons   Scottish

10

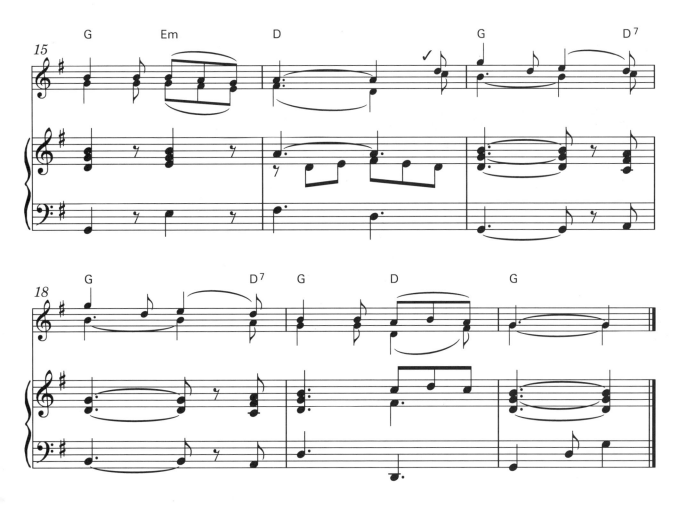

A drone accompaniment can give a good Scottish effect — try using the bass part given below instead of the piano accompaniment. This can be played on piano, but is also effective on an electric keyboard using one of the alternative voices. Try these suggestions and decide which you like best: cello, bassoon and saxophone. Some keyboards also have a bagpipe voice.

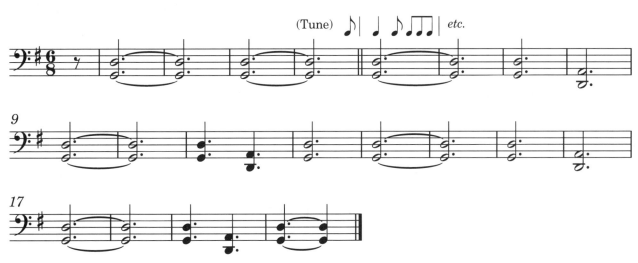

# Drink To Me Only    English

# Star of County Down  Irish

# Waltz   Schubert

Nb: The repeat signs in the Pupil's Book have been written out here.

# Cossack Dance    Pitts

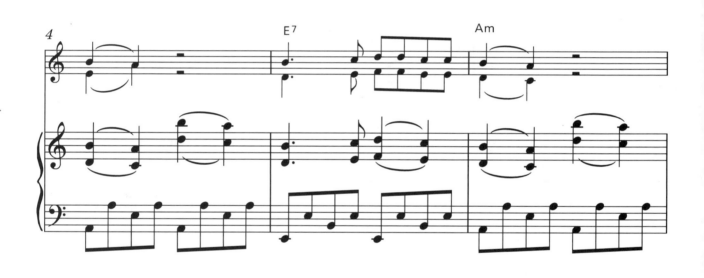

18

2 = optional alternative fingering

# Santa Lucia    Neopolitan

# Crombie's Boogie   Pitts

**Boogie-woogie** was a special type of early piano jazz music. It first became popular in America in the 1920's, then quickly became famous throughout the world and still is today. The pieces are usually 12 bars long, with rhythmic phrases using dotted notes as in this piece. The music here also uses the traditional pattern of chords called a **12 bar blues.**

There is another boogie in Recorder Duets from the Beginning Book 1 (Boogie Blues) and a blues in Book 3 (Beckett Blues).

# Pretty Peña    Mexican

# Portuguese Dance

Try adding a percussion accompaniment to enhance the music. Don't start playing until the first complete bar (i.e. after the recorders have played their first three notes). Listen carefully!

## Cielito Lindo  Mexican

Try adding some percussion accompaniment to enhance the music. Here are three ostinato patterns. You can use them in different ways: just one at a time, any two, or all three together!

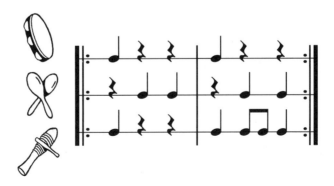

# Plaisir d'Amour  Martini

**2** = optional alternative fingering.

# The Saints

# O Waly Waly    English

*If Recorder 3 plays the melody from bar 8 then piano should repeat bars 1-8 of the accompaniment instead of bars 9-16. Then the Da Capo is played as normal.

34

# Czech Polka   J. Strauss

# Ragtime  Pitts

# Churchill's March

# Polka for Paula    Pitts

N.B.  The Pupil's Book uses a Da Capo, despite the Dal Segno needed here.

# March from Scipio    Handel

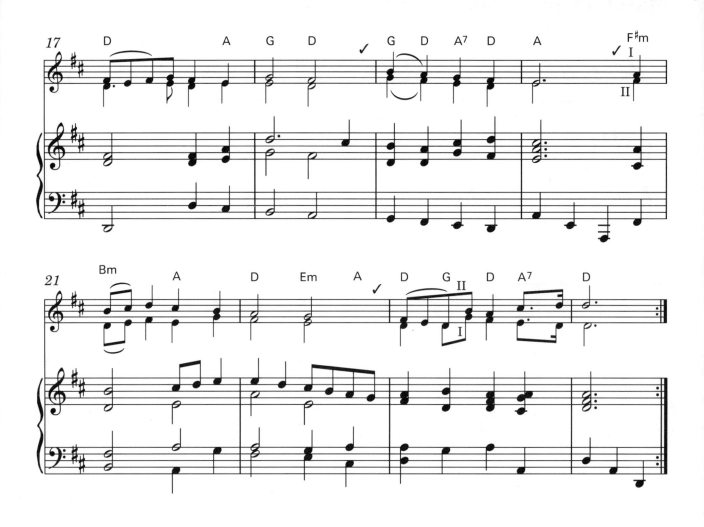

George Frederic **Handel** (1685-1759) was born in Germany and died in London. He spent most of his later life working in London and became a naturalised Englishman. He was a very successful theatrical composer and was as popular then as Andrew Lloyd Webber is today! He wrote many operas, including **Scipio,** from which this famous march comes. His oratorios, for vocal soloists, chorus and orchestra include the ever-popular Messiah. His orchestral works include the 'Water' Music and the 'Royal Fireworks' Music. He also wrote church music and music for the keyboard.

# Arima Samba     Pitts

**Not too fast** ( ♩ = 56 )

Accompaniment: the Pupil's Book includes the following ostinato suggestions for rhythm accompaniment. This will add flavour to the piece, whether or not the piano is used.

The **Samba** is a Brazilian dance with a basic two beats in each bar, strongly syncopated.

The rhythm patterns are usually in two-bar phrases. A special rhythmic feature is the anticipation of the first beat of the second bar of a two-bar pattern, so that this beat comes at the end of the previous bar and is tied over.

Try playing these rhythms, counting carefully.

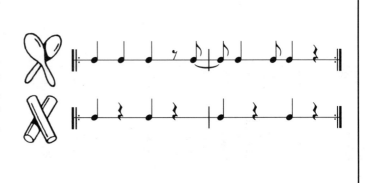

# Little Mazurka    Chopin

# Carman's Whistle    Elizabethan

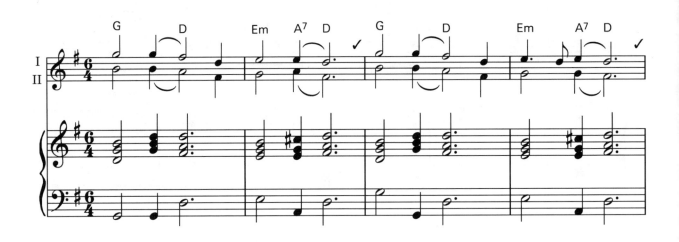

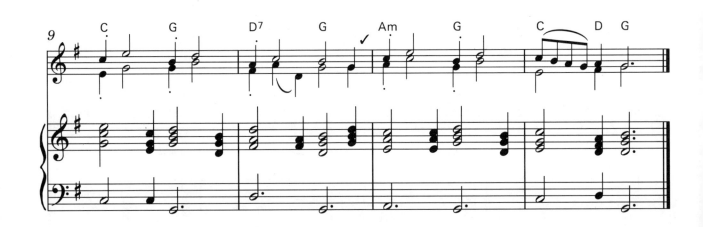

# Berceuse    Dvorak

# Cradle Song   Brahms

Johannes **Brahms** (1833-97) was a German composer. He wrote songs, including the famous 'Cradle Song', as well as many piano pieces. Brahms also wrote symphonies, concertos and several overtures and small orchestral works. Among the most popular was his 'Variations on a theme of Haydn' (the 'St Anthony Chorale').